G000099391

1 TIMES TABLE

0	× 1	=	0
1	× 1	=	1
2	× 1	=	2
3	× 1	=	3
4	× 1	=	4
5	× 1	=	5
6	× 1	=	6
7	× 1	=	7
8	× 1	=	8
9	× 1	=	9
10	× 1	=	10
11	× 1	=	11
12	× 1	=	12

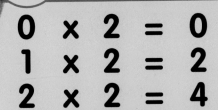

0	×	2	=	0
1	×	2	=	2
2	×	2	=	4
3	×	2	=	6
4	×	2	=	8
5	×	2	=	10
6	×	2	=	12
7	×	2	=	14
8	×	2	=	16
9	×	2	=	18
10	×	2	=	20
11	×	2	=	22
12	×	2	=	24

0	×	3	=	0
1	×	3	=	3
2	×	3	=	6
3	×	3	=	9
4	×	3	=	12
5	×	3	=	15
6	×	3	=	18
7	×	3	=	21
8	×	3	=	24
9	×	3	=	27
10	×	3	=	30
11	×	3	=	33
12	×	3	=	36

4 TIMES TABLE

0	×	4	=	0
1	×	4	=	4
2	×	4	=	8
3	×	4	=	12
4	×	4	=	16
5	×	4	=	20
6	×	4	=	24
7	×	4	=	28
8	×	4	=	32
9	×	4	=	36
10	×	4	=	40
11	×	4	=	44
12	×	4	=	48

5 TIMES TABLE

0	×	5	=	0
1	×	5	=	5
2	×	5	=	10
3	×	5	=	15
4	×	5	=	20
5	×	5	=	25
6	×	5	=	30
7	×	5	=	35
8	×	5	=	40
9	×	5	=	45
10	×	5	=	50
11	×	5	=	55
12	×	5	=	60

6 TIMES TABLE

0	×	6	=	0
1	×	6	=	6
2	×	6	=	12
3	×	6	=	18
4	×	6	=	24
5	×	6	=	30
6	×	6	=	36
7	×	6	=	42
8	×	6	=	48
9	×	6	=	54
10	×	6	=	60
11	×	6	=	66
12	×	6	=	72

7 TIMES TABLE

0	×	7	=	0
1	×	7	=	7
2	×	7	=	14
3	×	7	=	21
4	×	7	=	28
5	×	7	=	35
6	×	7	=	42
7	×	7	=	49
8	×	7	=	56
9	×	7	=	63
10	×	7	=	70
11	×	7	=	77
12	×	7	=	84

8 TIMES TABLE

0	× 8	=	0
1	× 8	=	8
2	× 8	=	16
3	× 8	=	24
4	× 8	=	32
5	× 8	=	40
6	× 8	=	48
7	× 8	=	56
8	× 8	=	64
9	× 8	=	72
10	× 8	=	80
11	× 8	=	88
12	× 8	=	96

9 TIMES TABLE

0	×	9	=	0
1	×	9	=	9
2	×	9	=	18
3	×	9	=	27
4	×	9	=	36
5	×	9	=	45
6	×	9	=	54
7	×	9	=	63
8	×	9	=	72
9	×	9	=	81
10	×	9	=	90
11	×	9	=	99
12	×	9	=	108

10 TIMES TABLE

0	×	10	=	0
1	×	10	=	10
2	×	10	=	20
3	×	10	=	30
4	×	10	=	40
5	×	10	=	50
6	×	10	=	60
7	×	10	=	70
8	×	10	=	80
9	×	10	=	90
10	×	10	=	100
11	×	10	=	110
12	×	10	=	120

11 TIMES TABLE

0	×	11	=	0
1	×	11	=	11
2	×	11	=	22
3	×	11	=	33
4	×	11	=	44
5	×	11	=	55
6	×	11	=	66
7	×	11	=	77
8	×	11	=	88
9	×	11	=	99
10	×	11	=	110
11	×	11	=	121
12	×	11	=	132

12 TIMES TABLE

0	× 12 =	0
1	× 12 =	12
2	× 12 =	24
3	× 12 =	36
4	× 12 =	48
5	× 12 =	60
6	× 12 =	72
7	× 12 =	84
8	× 12 =	96
9	× 12 =	108
10	× 12 =	120
11	× 12 =	132
12	× 12 =	144

INSTANT ANSWER

	1	2	3	4	5	6	7	8	9	10
0	0	0	0	0	0	0	0	0	0	0
1	1	2	3	4	5	6	7	8	9	10
2	2	4	6	8	10	12	14	16	18	20
3	3	6	9	12	15	18	21	24	27	30
4	4	8	12	16	20	24	28	32	36	40
5	5	10	15	20	25	30	35	40	45	50
6	6	12	18	24	30	36	42	48	54	60
7	7	14	21	28	35	42	49	56	63	70
8	8	16	24	32	40	48	56	64	72	80
9	9	18	27	36	45	54	63	72	81	90
10	10	20	30	40	50	60	70	80	90	100
11	11	22	33	44	55	66	77	88	99	110
12	12	24	36	48	60	72	84	96	108	120

NUMBER MATRIX

	11	12	13	14	15	16	17	18	19	20
0	0	0	0	0	0	0	0	0	0	0
1	11	12	13	14	15	16	17	18	19	20
2	22	24	26	28	30	32	34	36	38	40
3	33	36	39	42	45	48	51	54	57	60
4	44	48	52	56	60	64	68	72	76	80
5	55	60	65	70	75	80	85	90	95	100
6	66	72	78	84	90	96	102	108	114	120
7	77	84	91	98	105	112	119	126	133	140
8	88	96	104	112	120	126	136	144	152	160
9	99	108	117	126	135	144	153	162	171	180
10	110	120	130	140	150	160	170	180	190	200
11	121	132	143	154	165	176	187	198	209	220
12	132	144	156	168	180	192	204	216	228	240

First published in 2000
as a book and tape set by
Armadillo Books
An imprint of Bookmart Limited
Blaby Road, Wigston
Leicestershire, LE18 4SE
England

Reprinted 2001 (twice), 2003

ISBN 1-84322-076-8

Printed in Malaysia